The Picnic
Matching Shapes

by Lynn Maslen Kertell
pictures by Sue Hendra and John R. Maslen

Scholastic Inc.
New York • Toronto • London • Auckland • Sydney • Mexico City • New Delhi • Hong Kong • Buenos Aires

What a day for a picnic! Sally and
her brother, Mat, went to the park.

Seth took his brother Mac. Tanner took his brother Sam and sister Dot.

3

Mat and Sally brought their favorite

foods — grapes, oranges, and plums.

Mac and Seth packed peanut-
butter-and-jelly sandwiches.

Sam, Tanner, and Dot cut up
pizza and pie for the picnic.

Tanner asked, "Pizza, anyone?"
Sally said, "Who likes fruit?"

"Please have sandwiches, too!"
exclaimed Seth.

Seth, Sally, and Tanner
sat down to eat.

What a yummy lunch!

They had lots of fun eating circles, squares, and triangles.